UNTUNE THE SKY

Compiled by Helen Plotz

IMAGINATION'S OTHER PLACE

UNTUNE THE SKY

POEMS OF EMILY DICKINSON

THE EARTH IS THE LORD'S

UNTUNE THE SKY

Poems of Music and the Dance

COMPILED BY Helen Plotz

ILLUSTRATED WITH WOOD ENGRAVINGS BY

Clare Leighton

THOMAS Y. CROWELL COMPANY

NEW YORK

Grateful acknowledgment is made to the following publishers and authors
for permission to reprint copyrighted material:

GEORGE ALLEN & UNWIN, LTD., for seven lines of the chorus from "Where Shall Wisdom be Found" from *The Bacchae* by Euripides, translated by Dr. Gilbert Murray; the Canadian permission for "Hearing the Early Oriole" and "The Harper of Chao" by Po Chü-i, translated by Arthur Waley from *Translations from the Chinese.*

THE ATLANTIC MONTHLY COMPANY for "The Musician" by R. P. Lister, copyright 1956 by The Atlantic Monthly Company, Boston, Massachusetts; originally published in *The Atlantic.*

GEORGE BARKER for "On First Hearing Beethoven" from *Thirty Preliminary Poems* by George Barker, published by The Parton Press, London.

BASIL BLACKWELL & MOTT, LTD., for "Plato, a Musician" by Leontius, translated by A. J. Butler.

BRANDT & BRANDT for "On Hearing a Symphony of Beethoven" by Edna St. Vincent Millay from *The Buck in the Snow,* Harper & Brothers, copyright 1928 by Edna St. Vincent Millay, copyright renewed 1956 by Norma Millay.

JONATHAN CAPE, LTD., for "One and One" from *Poems in Wartime* by C. Day Lewis.

THE CRESSET PRESS for "M.S. Singing Frühlingsglaube in 1945" and "For Nijinsky's Tomb" by Frances Cornford.

CURTIS BROWN, LTD., for the selections by Ogden Nash: "The Birds," "The Introduction," and "Piano Tuner, Untune Me That Tune." "The Birds" originally appeared in *The New Yorker* Magazine, copyright 1935, 1950 by Ogden Nash; "Piano Tuner, Untune Me That Tune" copyright 1945 by The Curtis Publishing Company. Reprinted by permission of the author.

CHATTO & WINDUS and SYLVIA TOWNSEND WARNER for the Canadian permission for "Tudor Church Music" from *The Espalier* by Sylvia Townsend Warner.

ANDRE DEUTSCH, LTD., for the Canadian permission for "Music and Words" from *A Way of Looking* by Elizabeth Jennings.

NEW STATESMAN AND NATION for two stanzas from "Elegy on the Death of Mme. Anna Pavlova" by E. H. W. Meyerstein from *Best Poems of 1931* published by Thomas Moult, originally published in the *New Statesman and Nation,* 1931.

THE NEW YORKER for "Iberia" by Leo Kirschenbaum, by permission, copyright © 1955 The New Yorker Magazine, Inc.

THE NOONDAY PRESS for "Musician" by Louise Bogan from *Collected Poems.*

THE OPEN COURT PUBLISHING COMPANY for "The Swan and Goose" from *Aesop's Fables* translated by William Ellery Leonard.

OXFORD UNIVERSITY PRESS for "Homage to Vaslav Nijinsky" from *The Submerged Village and Other Poems* by James Kirkup, originally published by Oxford University Press, London; "Go to the Shine That's on a Tree" from *Undercliff* by Richard Eberhart; "At a Concert of Music" from *Collected Poems* by Conrad Aiken, copyright © 1953 by Conrad Aiken; "Willie Take Your Little Drum (Patapan)" from *The Oxford Book of Carols,* translated by Percy Dearmer, 1867–1936, reprinted by permission of The Oxford University Press, London; and selections from *Poems* by Gerard Manley Hopkins: excerpt from "The Habit of Perfection," "Henry Purcell," and excerpt from "On a Piece of Music." Reprinted by permission of Oxford University Press, Inc.

RANDOM HOUSE, INC., for excerpt from "The Desert Music" from *The Desert Music and Other Poems* by William Carlos Williams, copyright 1951 by William Carlos Williams; the American permission for "The Composer" from *The Collected Poetry of W. H. Auden,* copyright 1945 by W. H. Auden; and "Beethoven's Death Mask" and "The Swan" from *Collected Poems* by Stephen Spender, copyright 1934 by The Modern Library, Inc. Reprinted by permission of Random House, Inc.

RINEHART & COMPANY, INC., for "The Clavichord" from *The Lion and the Rose* by May Sarton, copyright 1948 by May Sarton; and the American permission for "Music and Words" by Elizabeth Jennings from *A Way of Looking,* copyright 1955 by Elizabeth Jennings. Reprinted by permission of Rinehart & Company, Inc.

SIEGFRIED SASSOON AND WILLIAM HEINEMANN, LTD., for the Canadian permission for "Sheldonian Soliloquy (during Bach's B Minor Mass)" and "A Music Critic Anticipates Eternity" from *Satirical Poems* by Siegfried Sassoon, published by William Heinemann Ltd.

CHARLES SCRIBNER'S SONS for selections by Rolfe Humphries: "Harp Music," copyright 1954 by Rolfe Humphries, reprinted from *Poems Collected and New* by Rolfe Humphries; "Static," copyright 1937 by Rolfe Humphries, reprinted from *Poems Collected and New* by Rolfe Humphries; "Variations on a Theme by Francis Kilvert" from *The Wind of Time* by Rolfe Humphries, copyright 1949 by Rolfe Humphries. For "Mozart Perhaps" from *Poems Old and New* by John Hall Wheelock, copyright 1956 by John Hall Wheelock; "Symphony: First Movement" from *Poems Old and New* by John Hall Wheelock, copyright 1956 by John Hall Wheelock; "Vaudeville Dancer,"

TO Milton
AND TO Our Children
Elizabeth, Paul, Sarah,
and John

PREFACE

Music and poetry are so interwoven, one with the other, that they can be described in almost the same terms; indeed, in their early history, music, dance, and poetry were one. Music is surely the most universal of the arts, and, like the instinctive drives which underlie our actions, it is a part of all human experience everywhere.

The arts are often defined almost as though they were truly interchangeable—we hear that architecture is frozen music, that music is colorful, or that there are pictures in sound. These confusing and misleading definitions leave out the primary qualities of both kinds of art. Painting, sculpture, and architecture are essentially arts of space; music and poetry are arts of time. Only dancing partakes for a moment of both space and time.

We can move physically through space but not through time. It may be that it is time which gives to music, as to poetry, the power to take us away from our sole selves into the eternal moment. Music heard becomes music remembered and each of us carries within himself all of the music he has known. And time present and time future are in music. Jazz is part of some modern poetry and Sibelius as well as Händel may inspire a poet.

History is another of the arts of time and our music is our history. It has always been so. In its simplest sense our history is "Yankee Doodle" and the American Revolution. In a deeper, but not a different sense, it is "Go Down Moses" and the "Battle Hymn of the Republic."

So too with religion. From the time the morning stars sang

together, music and dancing have played a part in all religions of the world, Eastern as well as Western and all men have praised God with music and dancing.

The poems gathered here are poems about music and dancing in all of their aspects. There are five divisions, all overlapping one another. The first section is devoted to poems about instruments, the second to songs and their singers. The third section is concerned with composers and the fourth with the dance. Last of all are poems about the transcendent power of music.

Music and dancing are bound up in all of life; in fun and humor, in play, in solitude and companionship, in work and in idleness, in war and death and ugliness, as well as in hope and in love.

ACKNOWLEDGMENTS

My first and deepest thanks to my husband and to our older children who read and talked and listened and sometimes fought over both music and poetry. Our daughter Elizabeth imbued me with her devotion to the poetry and music of the Elizabethan era. She found many poems and did much leg-work and typing.

Fannie Gittleman coped valiantly and well with all the myriad details.

Dorothy Plum welcomed me to the Vassar Library.

My thanks to David McCord for revising "Litany" for this book.

Mr. Wilson, the scholarly bookseller of Bumpus', in London, extended to me the same courtesy and interest that have helped so many others.

I am indebted to Theresa Wolfson Wood who has read the entire manuscript and who has made many fruitful suggestions.

CONTENTS

SECTION 1 · All Instruments

SECTION 2 · Singing over the Earth

SECTION 3 · One God Is God of Both

SECTION 4 · Poet to Dancer

SECTION 5 · Music Shall Untune the Sky

ALL INSTRUMENTS

ALL INSTRUMENTS

When there were giants in the earth in the days before the Flood, Jubal was the father of all such as handled the harp and organ; when the gods walked among men, Pan, the god of the forests, gathered reeds from the river bank and bound them together into pipes. Musical instruments were surely among the first inventions in the world. The harp, the lyre, and the flute go so far back in history that even the Hebrews and the Greeks did not know the names of their real inventors.

Poetry was music once and poets, besides being singers, were players on the harp or the lyre. Poets are still singing and surely there will never be a "last minstrel." Not many poets today play the harp but poems often identify the instruments with their players or with Nature. Shelley's plea to the west wind, "Make me thy lyre even as the forest is," is echoed by a modern poet, Babette Deutsch, asking who "summons the son of the morning from this hollow wood."

Many of the poems in this section are about players, about fiddlers, pianists (or players of chopsticks!), and about other

3

"Sons of Art." Sometimes the poet speaks in the person of a player, sometimes he stands apart and listens to the jazz pianist or to the man with the blue guitar or to the old harper.

That instruments have characters of their own seems self-evident and yet, a good deal of what we feel about certain instruments comes to us from poetry as well as from music itself. Does not the trumpet in Händel's Messiah *stir us more deeply when we hear: "The trumpet shall sound"? And surely, Coleridge's "lonely flute" captures the poignant essence of that instrument.*

There are poems here about teachers as well as performers and about street musicians as well as great artists. To the poet the country fiddler is as interesting as the virtuoso, the little girl at the piano as serious as Paderewski. The poet does not usually attempt to criticize performance, but to take part in it imaginatively at whatever level he chooses. Jubal and Pan are his fathers too.

from THE DESERT MUSIC

             the music! the
music! as when Casals struck
and held a deep cello tone
and I am speechless

            .   .   .   .   .

Now the music volleys through as in
a lonely moment I hear it. Now it is all
about me. The dance! The verb detaches itself
seeking to become articulate

            And I could not help thinking
            of the wonders of the brain that
            hears that music and of our
            skill sometimes to record it.

                        William Carlos Williams

THE MUSICIAN

How loudly and how surely the musician plays!
He was born piping in the beginning of his days;
Now he is elderly, with a small white beard,
He pipes as loudly as his parents feared—

But pipes more surely than his parents heard.
This the piping of a blithe and white-beard bird,
Perched on a pole with summer in his heart,
But drilled in all the discipline of art.

This is the music for the celebration of the sun;
Joy with a shade of sorrow, but of rancor none.
Strange that a small musician with a beard of snow
Should put all youth into his piping so.

And in deep memory his bent fingers play
Long after the sunset of his piping day.

R. P. Lister

PSALM 150

Praise ye the Lord.
Praise God in his sanctuary,
praise him in the firmament of his power.
Praise him for his mighty acts,
praise him according to his excellent greatness.
Praise him with the sound of the trumpet,
praise him with the psaltery and harp.
Praise him with the timbrel and dance,
praise him with stringed instruments and organs.
Praise him upon the loud cymbals,
praise him upon the high sounding cymbals.
Let every thing that hath breath praise the Lord.
Praise ye the Lord.

IN GRATO JUBILO

(*And they sung a new song*. Revelation: 5, 9.)

Unfold unfold
Thou beaten-gold
Harmonic third
Beyond the word
Beyond the long
Unsung the song
Beyond the song

From the sea and the sky and the lean of the land
And the world in the round
To the way of the head and the way of the hand
And the way of the soul is the way of the sound

In jubilee
In jubilo
Beneath this tree
The waters flow

The cry unanswered in the cry as joy and sorrow pass:
The woodwind singing through the wood: no shadow on the grass

Though man was born a rebel
Rebellion in his face
O voices in the treble
Yet shall he win to grace
O voices in the bass
Yet shall he find his place
Time in the space of space

Soft as the summer night along the diapason shore
The far forgotten music of the world is at the door
And open open open cry the voices as before

Symbol symbol symbol: symbol in the sky!
The light of stars the gravid sun the watchful eye!
Sound sound sound: sound of the trumpet! Blow
The sound as when a time of singing willed it so!

David McCord

NOTE: *The essential text of this poem was the basis of an occasional cantata performed in Boston in honor of Serge Koussevitzky on his retirement as Conductor of the Boston Symphony Orchestra in 1949. The music for stanzas 1 and 3 was composed by Lukas Foss, conductor of the piece; for stanza 2 by Herbert Fromm; 4 by Allen Sapp; 5 by Gardner Read; 6 by Daniel Pinkham; 7 by Irving Fine. The poem as printed here has been adapted and rearranged by the author.*

THE PLAYERS ASK FOR A BLESSING
ON THE PSALTERIES AND ON THEMSELVES

THREE VOICES [*together*]. Hurry to bless the hands that play,
The mouths that speak, the notes and strings,
O masters of the glittering town!
O! lay the shrilly trumpet down,
Though drunken with the flags that sway
Over the ramparts and the towers,
And with the waving of your wings.

FIRST VOICE. Maybe they linger by the way.
One gathers up his purple gown;
One leans and mutters by the wall—
He dreads the weight of mortal hours.

SECOND VOICE. O no, O no! they hurry down
Like plovers that have heard the call.

THIRD VOICE. O kinsmen of the Three in One,
O kinsmen, bless the hands that play.
The notes they waken shall live on
When all this heavy history's done;
Our hands, our hands must ebb away.

THREE VOICES [*together*]. The proud and careless notes live on,
But bless our hands that ebb away.

W. B. Yeats

10

PLATO, A MUSICIAN

When Orpheus died, some Muse the lyre still fingered:
    But Plato passed, and mute the viol lies:
For in his heart and in his hand there lingered
    Some remnant of the ancient melodies.

Leontius
Translated by A. J. Butler

ON HEARING A FLUTE AT NIGHT FROM THE WALL OF SHOU-HSIANG

The sand below the border-mountain lies like snow,
And the moon like frost beyond the city-wall,
And someone somewhere, playing a flute,
Has made the soldiers homesick all night long.

Li Yi
Translated by Witter Bynner

11

CORINNA

When to her lute Corinna sings,
Her voice revives the leaden strings,
And doth in highest notes appear
As any challenged echo clear.
But when she doth of mourning speak,
E'en with her sighs the strings do break.

And as her lute doth live or die,
Led by her passion, so must I;
For when of pleasure she doth sing,
My thoughts enjoy a sudden spring;
But if she doth of sorrow speak,
E'en from my heart the strings do break.

Thomas Campion

TO HIS LUTE

My lute, be as thou wast when thou didst grow
With thy green mother in some shady grove,
When immelodious winds but made thee move,
And birds on thee their ramage did bestow.
Sith that dear voice, which did thy sounds approve,
Which used in such harmonious strains to flow,
Is reft from earth to tune those spheres above,
What art thou but a harbinger of woe?
Thy pleasing notes be pleasing notes no more,
But orphan wailings to the fainting ear;
Each stop a sigh, each sound draws forth a tear,
Be therefore silent as in woods before:
     Or, if that any hand to touch thee deign,
     Like widowed turtle still her loss complain.

William Drummond

from THE TAMING OF THE SHREW

"Why, then thou canst not break her to the lute?"
"Why no, for she hath broke the lute to me.
I did but tell her she mistook her frets,
And bow'd her hand to teach her fingering;
When, with a most impatient, devilish spirit,
'Frets call you these?' quoth she; 'I'll fume with them:'
And with that word she struck me on the head,
And through the instrument my pate made way;
And there I stood amazéd for a while,
As on a pillory, looking through the lute,
While she did call me rascal fiddler,
And twangling Jack, with twenty such vile terms,
As had she studied to misuse me so."

William Shakespeare

ONE AND ONE

I remember, as if it were yesterday,
Watching that girl from the village lay
The fire in a room where sunlight poured,
And seeing, in the annexe beyond, M. play
A prelude of Bach on his harpsichord.

I can see his face now, heavy and numb
With resignation to the powers that come
At his touch meticulous, smooth as satin,
Firm as hammers: I can hear the air thrum
With notes like sun-motes in a twinkling pattern.

Her task there fetched from the girl the innate
Tingling response of glass to a note:
She fitted the moment, too, like a glove,
Who deft and submissive knelt by the grate
Bowed as if in the labour of love.

Their orbits touched not: but the pure submission
Of each gave value and definition
To a snapshot printed in that morning's sun.
From any odd corner we may start a vision
Proving that one and one make One.

C. Day Lewis

15

TUDOR CHURCH MUSIC

Here in the minster tower
I sit alone,
While to mind's ear old books
Mumble and drone;
And the warm sun slants in
Over the cold stone.

Through the long afternoon
I hear the clock
Preach to the empty church:
Tick-tock. Tick-tock.
O, a rare text to expound
To a sleeping flock!

The patient organist
Who scrolled this clef;
The boy who drew him horned
On Gibbons in F;
Singers and hearers all
Are dumb and deaf—

'Dumb and deaf, dead and dust,'
Confirms the clock.
And life seems so far off
That at the shock
I see my calm hand start,
When footsteps knock

Upon stair. Holiday-makers
Out on a trip
To whom the verger propounds
Each trusty quip,
While, mute, they fidget together
In uneasy fellowship.

And only when they are gone
Do I doff the mask
Of the scholar deep in his book:
'Did they see me?' I ask,
'Or am I, too, a ghost?' and so
Turn once more to my task.

Sylvia Townsend Warner

THE CLAVICHORD

She keeps her clavichord
As others keep delight, too light
To breathe, the secret word
No lover ever heard
Where the pure spirit lives
And garlands weaves.

To make the pure notes sigh
(Not of a human grief, too brief)
A sigh of such fragility
Her fingers' sweet agility
Must hold the horizontal line
In the stern power of design.

The secret breathed within
And never spoken, woken
By music; the garlands in
Her hands no one has seen.
She wreathes the air with green
And weaves the stillness in.

May Sarton

RECORDERS IN ITALY

It was amusing on that antique grass,
Seated halfway between the green and blue,
To waken music gentle and extinct

Under the old walls where the daisies grew
Sprinkled in cinquecento style, as though
Archangels might have stepped there yesterday

But it was we, mortal and young, who strolled
And fluted quavering music, for a day
Casual heirs of all we looked upon.

Such pipers of the emerald afternoon
Could only be the heirs of perfect time
When every leaf distinctly brushed with gold

Listened to Primavera speaking flowers.
Those scherzos stumble now; our journeys run
To harsher hillsides, rockier declensions.

Obligatory climates call us home.
And so shall clarity of cypresses,
Unfingered by necessity, become

Merely the ghost of half-remembered trees,
A trick of sunlight flattering the mind?—
There were four recorders sweet upon the wind.

Adrienne Cecile Rich

ELIZABETH AT THE PIANO

It is memory speaking, preternaturally clear,
Awake, remote: the piano playing
Through the dark midwinter afternoon,
The string-filled music at four o'clock
Chopin, Mozart, Suppé.

                             What I remember
Of that lilac-breathing house
Are flames against dark windows,
And beyond the curtained door
A young girl seated at the square piano.

                          Listen: I hear
The walking metronome: one, two, one, two,
Then the minuet. It is the practice hour,
The pendulum swinging between the walls,
Upstairs and down.

                           There is the smell
of wet lath, of rain-darkened plaster.

Behind the house the wintry lilac forest,
And behind the coals in the grate
The winter sunset smolders.

                          Is that flame
The sunset breaking through the fire?
One can almost hear the pendulum walk the stairs,
The lonely footfall, then the minuet.

Awake, remote, the house stands in gray—
Clouded brick, leaning through gray midwinter sunset air,
The firelight failing behind the curtained door.
And at the piano in the shadowed room
The dust-filled metronome
Clicks: it is the practice hour.
                              And is that face,
The sunset glancing through darkness
Over white and rose, and caught within
Moonlight of yellow hair, her face?
Is the child there?

Faintly, the minuet—or is that sound a bell
Ringing, unanswered, or someone calling
A child's name down the street?
The house looms, then fades in the wind;
It has begun to snow, the piano is glazed with sleet,
Then frost; it is snowing everywhere.

Horace Gregory

from RECITAL

Sognando

In the motionless haze of interior heat
Diluted by music, illusion is sweet.
At two grand pianos two children are playing,
A fleeting and nebulous spell they are laying,
Dressed for enchantment in dim summer blue
With the misty aloofness of flowers in dew,
And the figures and instruments both are alike
As the clearly identical notes that they strike—
A grouping of pattern for tapestried pageant,
The coming to life of a delicate legend
Of two with fair hair who did dreamily drive
Twin ebony creatures profoundly alive,
Through the afternoon air blue as water on stone.
. . . Or is it one child who is playing alone
In front of a mirror which muses on magic
And gives back an image, the image of music?

Louise Townsend Nicholl

22

THE HARPER OF CHAO

The singers have hushed their notes of clear song:
The red sleeves of the dancers are motionless.
Hugging his lute, the old harper of Chao
Rocks and sways as he touches the five chords.
The loud notes swell and scatter abroad:
"Sa, sa," like wind blowing the rain.
The soft notes dying almost to nothing:
"Ch'ieh, ch'ieh," like the voice of ghosts talking.
Now as glad as the magpie's lucky song:
Again bitter as the gibbon's ominous cry.
His ten fingers have no fixed note:
Up and down—*kung, chih,* and *yü*.[1]
And those who sit and listen to the tune he plays
Of soul and body lose the mastery.
And those who pass that way as he plays the tune,
Suddenly stop and cannot raise their feet.

Alas, alas that the ears of common men
Should love the modern and not love the old.
Thus it is that the harp in the green window
Day by day is covered deeper with dust.

[1] Tonic, dominant, and superdominant of the ancient five-note scale.

Po Chü-i
Translated by Arthur Waley

from JUBILATE AGNO

For the feast of Trumpets should be kept up that being the most
   direct and acceptable of all instruments;
For the Trumpet of God is a blessed intelligence and so are all
   the instruments in Heaven.
For God the father Almighty plays upon the Harp of stupendous
   magnitude and melody.
For innumerable Angels fly out at every touch and his tune is a
   work of creation.

Christopher Smart

VARIATION ON A THEME BY FRANCIS KILVERT

The Welsh harp has no silver string,
And it is played on the left shoulder.
And the harpers all are older
Than the counsellors of the king.

And they are becoming rare,
Those gray and bearded men
With young hands and long fingers,

But every here and there,
By glade or coombe or glen,
One of them lingers

Remote from all known ways
Save those that music clears
Through ash and sycamore
To the door of their dwelling.

Whenever one of them plays,
Whoever hears him hears
Most beautiful old airs.

They are poor of purse; they rise
May mornings, very early,
And tradesmen think they are surly
In spite of the wrinkled eyes
Scored by their years of smiling.

Rolfe Humphries

BLOW, BUGLE, BLOW

The splendour falls on castle walls
 And snowy summits old in story:
The long light shakes across the lakes,
 And the wild cataract leaps in glory.
Blow, bugle, blow, set the wild echoes flying,
Blow, bugle; answer, echoes, dying, dying, dying.

O hark, O hear! how thin and clear,
 And thinner, clearer, farther going!
O sweet and far from cliff and scar
 The horns of Elfland faintly blowing!
Blow, let us hear the purple glens replying:
Blow, bugle; answer, echoes, dying, dying, dying.

O love, they die in yon rich sky,
 They faint on hill or field or river:
Our echoes roll from soul to soul,
 And grow for ever and for ever.
Blow, bugle, blow, set the wild echoes flying,
And answer, echoes, answer, dying, dying, dying.

Alfred, Lord Tennyson

THE TIN-WHISTLE PLAYER

'Tis long since, long since, since I heard
A tin-whistle played,
And heard the tunes, the ha'penny tunes
That nobody made!

The tunes that were before Cendfind
And Cir went Ireland's rounds—
That were before the surety
That strings have given sounds!

And now is standing in the mist,
And jigging backward there,
Shrilling with fingers and with breath,
A tin-whistle player!

He has hare's eyes, a long face rimmed
Around with badger-grey;
Aimless, like cries of mountain birds
The tunes he has to play—

The tunes that are for stretches bare,
And men whose lives are lone—
And I had seen that face of his
Sculptured on cross of stone,
That long face, in a place of graves
With nettles overgrown.

Padraic Colum

MUSICIAN

Where have these hands been,
By what delayed,
That so long stayed
Apart from the thin

Strings which they now grace
With their lonely skill?
Music and their cool will
At last interlace.

Now with great ease, and slow,
The thumb, the finger, the strong
Delicate hand plucks the long
String it was born to know.

And, under the palm, the string
Sings as it wished to sing.

Louise Bogan

A FIDDLER

Once was a fiddler. Play could he
Sweet as a bird in an almond tree;
Fingers and strings—they seemed to be
Matched, in a secret conspiracy.
Up slid his bow, paused lingeringly;
Music's self was its witchery.

In his stooping face it was plain to see
How close to dream is a soul set free—
A half-found world;
And company.

His fiddle is broken.
Mute is he.
But a bird sings on in the almond tree.

Walter de la Mare

FIDDLER JONES

The earth keeps some vibration going
There in your heart, and that is you.
And if the people find you can fiddle,
Why, fiddle you must, for all your life.
What do you see, a harvest of clover?
Or a meadow to walk through to the river?
The wind's in the corn; you rub your hands
For beeves hereafter ready for market;
Or else you hear the rustle of skirts
Like the girls when dancing at Little Grove.
To Cooney Potter a pillar of dust
Or whirling leaves meant ruinous drouth;
They looked to me like Red-Head Sammy
Stepping it off, to "Toor-a-Loor."
How could I till my forty acres
Not to speak of getting more,
With a medley of horns, bassoons and piccolos
Stirred in my brain by crows and robins
And the creak of a wind-mill—only these?
And I never started to plow in my life
That some one did not stop in the road
And take me away to a dance or picnic.
I ended up with forty acres;
I ended up with a broken fiddle—
And a broken laugh, and a thousand memories,
And not a single regret.

Edgar Lee Masters

"I WON'T BE MY FATHER'S JACK"

I won't be my father's Jack,
I won't be my mother's Jill,
I will be the fiddler's wife
And have music when I will.
 T'other little tune,
 T'other little tune,
 Prithee, love, play me
 T'other little tune.

Nursery Rhyme

"O I WON'T LEAD A HOMELY LIFE"

(*To an old air*)

"O I won't lead a homely life
As father's Jack and mother's Jill,
But I will be a fiddler's wife,
   With music mine at will!
      Just a little tune,
      Another one soon,
   As I merrily fling my fill!"

And she became a fiddler's Dear,
And merry all day she strove to be;
And he played and played afar and near,
   But never at home played he
      Any little tune
      Or late or soon;
   And sunk and sad was she!

Thomas Hardy

"JACKY, COME GIVE ME THY FIDDLE"

Jacky, come give me thy fiddle
   If ever you mean to thrive.
Nay, I'll not give my fiddle
   To any man alive.
If I should give my fiddle,
   They'll think that I'm gone mad,
For many a joyful day
   My fiddle and I have had.

Nursery Rhyme

LISZT

The Abbé Liszt
Hit the piano with his fist.
That was the way
He used to play.

E. C. Bentley

from ITALIAN OPERA

In Days of Old, when *Englishmen* were—*Men,*
Their Musick, like themselves, was grave and plain;
The manly Trumpet, and the simple Reed,
Alike with *Citizen* and *Swain* agreed;
Whose Songs, in lofty Sense, but humble Verse,
Their Loves and Wars alternately rehearse;
Sung by themselves, their homely Cheer to crown,
In Tunes from Sire to Son deliver'd down.
     But now, since *Britains* are become polite,
Since Few can *read,* and Fewer still can *write;*

    .   .   .   .   .

Since *Masquerades* and *Op'ras* made their Entry,
And *Heydegger* reign'd *Guardian* of our Gentry;
A hundred various Instruments combined,
And foreign *Songsters* in the Concert join:
The *Gallick Horn* whose winding Tube in vain
Pretends to emulate the *Trumpet's* Strain;
The *shrill-ton'd Fiddle,* and the *warbling Flute,*
The *grave Bassoon, deep base,* and *tinkling Lute,*
The *jingling Spinnet,* and the *full-mouth'd Drum,*
A *Roman Capon,* and *Venetian Strum,*
All league, melodious Nonsense to dispense,
And give us *Sound,* and *Show,* instead of *Sense;*
In unknown Tongues mysterious Dullness chant,
Make Love in *Tune,* or *thro' the Gamut rant.*

James Miller

35

STRING QUARTET

Who have no heaven come
Into the hall that passively receives
Their fluttering chattering quotidian selves,
The grieving mind and the deceiving heart.
Then they recede, as who should bow before
The entering instruments.
These find their places,
And all is garden and is grace, is
Eden, animal and innocent.
The violins and the viola cradle restless chins,
The serious cello's blonde body glows.
How faithful are the dog-eared scores, and how
The bows lift, scenting music!
Now, coolly as a flower,
Silence unfolds, as paradise
Begins.

    Fingers prance on the strings,
    Bows dance in air,
    Time is undone even where time grows,
    Blossoming like a tapestry's blue and rose,
    Vanishing like its colors at day's close:
    Blossoming, fading, vanishing, only to spring
    Up as a fountain tossing a crystal ball
    On the tips of the water's fingers.

They watch it fall,
The impalpable sphere striped with day and night;
Will it roll away out of the hall,
Or tossed once more
Leap into the sky
And be lost?
Some cough, some sigh, or stir in their chairs,
Some stare
At the floor or the ceiling, a few close their eyes.
Time is the hairs of a horse stroking the gut of a sheep,
Time is a hole in the carpet, is dust on the lamp, is a cramp in the
    knee.
Time is nothing to see.
But what is it summons
The son of the morning from this hollow wood
In his first radiance, summons
The daughters of music too in theirs?
What temporal marvel unmakes time, that here
Dread peers over the brink into the gulf
And does not shrink,
Love sees how vilely it must live
And smiles?

Babette Deutsch

SYMPHONY: FIRST MOVEMENT

Faintly at first, and low,
The horns sing lamentation; answering cries
From flute and oboe weave obscure replies;
Through the forest of the spirit
Old fretful winds and murmurs breathe and blow;
Secrets we all inherit,
Sorrows, deep at the core of Being grounded,
Well up again, and flow;
The truce that bound it
Is torn away, Time's wound is bared anew.
Hear, O my spirit!
The violins begin their proud complaint
In the desert of the world.

John Hall Wheelock

from TWELFTH NIGHT

If music be the food of love, play on!
Give me excess of it, that, surfeiting,
The appetite may sicken, and so die.
That strain again! It had a dying fall.
O, it came o'er my ear like the sweet sound
That breathes upon a bank of violets,
Stealing and giving odour. Enough! no more!
'Tis not so sweet now as it was before.

William Shakespeare

from THE BOWER OF BLISS

Eftsoons they heard a most melodious sound,
    Of all that mote delight a dainty ear,
Such as at once might not on living ground,
    Save in this paradise, be heard elsewhere:
    Right hard it was, for wight, which did it hear,
To read, what manner music that mote be;
    For all that pleasing is to living ear,
Was there consorted in one harmony,
Birds, voices, instruments, winds, waters, all agree.

The joyous birds, shrouded in cheerful shade,
    Their notes unto the voice attempered sweet;
Th' angelical soft trembling voices made
    To th' instruments divine respondence meet;
    The silver sounding instruments did meet
With the bass murmur of the waters' fall;
    The waters' fall with difference discreet,
Now soft, now loud, unto the wind did call;
The gentle warbling wind low answered to all.

Edmund Spenser

from THE TEMPEST

Be not afeard. The isle is full of noises,
Sounds and sweet airs, that give delight and hurt not.
Sometimes a thousand twangling instruments
Will hum about mine ears, and sometimes voices
That, if I then had wak'd after long sleep,
Will make me sleep again;

William Shakespeare

STATIC

All the foul fiends and demons of the air,
All the dark atmosphere's benighted host,
Banshees in rage, hobgoblins in despair,
Furious ghoul, mad imp, unbrageous ghost,
Asmodeus, Abaddona, Ahriman,
Belial, Cacodemon,—call the roll
Of succubus and vampire, all the clan,
Nis, kobold, dwerger, gnome, djinn, oufe, and troll.

How they all howl and chatter, whine and squall,
Halloo and whistle, yell, snort, gaggle, screak,
Knock, click, and clash, and stammer! How they all
Denounce themselves poor creatures, vain and weak,
Who with intemperate crepitation sue
To keep sweet crooning sounds from me and you.

Rolfe Humphries

PIANO TUNER, UNTUNE ME THAT TUNE

I regret that before people can be reformed they have to be
  sinners,
And that before you have pianists in the family you have to have
  beginners.
When it comes to beginners' music
I am not enthusic,
And when listening to something called "An Evening in My Doll
  House," or "The Bee and the Clover,"
Why I'd like just once to hear it played all the way through, in-
  stead of that hard part near the end over and over.
Have you noticed about little fingers?
When they hit a sour note, they lingers.
And another thing about little fingers, they are always strawberry-
  jammed or cranberry-jellied-y,
And "Chopsticks" is their favorite melody,
And if there is one man who I hope his dentist was a sadist and
  all his teeth were brittle ones,
It is he who invented "Chopsticks" for the little ones.
My good wishes are less than frugal
For him who started the little ones going boogie-woogal,
But for him who started the little ones picking out "Chopsticks"
  on the ivories,
Well, I wish him a thousand harems of a thousand wives apiece,
  and a thousand little ones by each wife, and each little one
  playing "Chopsticks" twenty-four hours a day in all the nurs-
  eries of all his harems, or wiveries.

Ogden Nash

RECIPE FOR AN EVENING MUSICALE

Candles. Red tulips, sixty cents the bunch.
Two lions, Grade B. A newly tuned piano.
No cocktails, but a dubious kind of punch,
Lukewarm and weak. A harp and a soprano.

The Lullaby of Brahms. Somebody's cousin
From Forest Hills, addicted to the pun.
Two dozen gentlemen; ladies, three dozen,
Earringed and powdered. Sandwiches at one.

The ashtrays few, the ventilation meagre.
Shushes to greet the late-arriving guest.
Or quell the punch-bowl group. A young man eager
To render "Danny Deever," by request.

And sixty people trying to relax
On little rented chairs with gilded backs.

Phyllis McGinley

from COME YE SONS OF ART

Come, ye Sons of Art, come away,
Tune all your voices and instruments play,
To celebrate this triumphant day.

Sound the trumpet, till around
You make the listening shores rebound.
On the sprightly hautboy play,
All the instruments of joy
That skilful numbers can employ
To celebrate the glories of this day.

Come, ye Sons of Art, come away,
Tune all your voices and instruments play,
To celebrate this triumphant day.

Strike the viol, touch the lute,
Wake the harp, inspire the flute,
Sing your patroness's praise
In cheerful and harmonious lays.

Henry Purcell

SINGING OVER THE EARTH

SINGING OVER
THE EARTH

None of us can imagine a world that has no singing in it. Poets have always been singers. In earliest times all poems were sung and there was no separation of poems and songs until comparatively recent times.

Nursery rhymes, which are almost as old as our language itself, are meant to be sung or chanted; there are many songs that are somehow handed down from one generation of children to the next.

The knowledge that singing came first is deeply imbedded in all of us. As Kipling says,

> *"When 'Omer smote 'is bloomin' lyre*
> *He'd 'eard men sing by land an' sea";*

and to describe verse as "singing" is high praise.

By Shakespeare's time verse and song had developed independently though some of our loveliest songs were written in the

Elizabethan years. Shakespeare's own verse is full of music.
There is so much musical imagery in his plays and poems that
it has been suggested that he was a trained musician. It is likely,
though, that Shakespeare did not have more formal musical edu-
cation than did the poets and actors and courtiers who were his
friends, for in those days almost everyone could hold his own in
an impromptu madrigal and play at least one instrument. Shake-
speare used the songs and dances of his country childhood and
the music that was all about him in the houses of his friends and
the taverns and theaters of London, and wove that music into the
fabric of all his poetry.

The Elizabethan poets have been called "a nest of singing birds,"
perhaps because so many of them wrote poems to music. One
of these poets, Thomas Campion, was indeed a musical scholar
and composer, and he set a standard that few have achieved in
the years that have passed since he wrote his songs.

The poems in this section are about songs and singers. Because
a lovely singing voice seems to be a gift of God, singers have
been extravagantly eulogized; conversely, harsh singing has
called forth far more venom and satire than has inept playing
or clumsy dancing.

At its best, singing seems to be as untutored and effortless and as
direct as the song of a bird or of an angel, and poets have mir-
rored in these verses the simplicity and the beauty of the songs
they have loved.

MUSIC AND WORDS

No human singing can
   Express itself without
Words that usurp the sounds
   That pour forth from the throat.
But when the music ends
   There lie within our minds
Thoughts that refuse to fit,
   That will not sing or scan
Or alter what they mean.

Yet we believe in song
   Some meaning that no word
Can catch is finely caught,
   That music is a state
Where truth is overheard.
   But we are wrong, are wrong:
Thoughts still are shaped of hard
   Unalterable stuff
We think we can forget
   If we sing loud enough.

Elizabeth Jennings

LAURA

Rose-cheeked Laura, come;
Sing thou smoothly with thy beauty's
Silent music, either other
    Sweetly gracing.

Lovely forms do flow
From concent divinely framed;
Heaven is music, and thy beauty's
    Birth is heavenly.

These dull notes we sing
Discords need for helps to grace them;
Only beauty purely loving
    Knows no discord;

But still moves delight,
Like clear springs renewed by flowing,
Ever perfect, ever in them-
    Selves eternal.

Thomas Campion

THE SOLITARY REAPER

Behold her, single in the field,
      Yon solitary Highland Lass!
Reaping and singing by herself;
      Stop here, or gently pass!
Alone she cuts and binds the grain,
And sings a melancholy strain;
O listen! for the Vale profound
Is overflowing with the sound.

No Nightingale did ever chaunt
      More welcome notes to weary bands
Of travellers in some shady haunt,
      Among Arabian sands:
A voice so thrilling ne'er was heard
In spring-time from the Cuckoo-bird,
Breaking the silence of the seas
Among the farthest Hebrides.

Will no one tell me what she sings?—
      Perhaps the plaintive numbers flow
For old, unhappy, far-off things,
      And battles long ago:
Or is it some more humble lay,
Familiar matter of to-day?
Some natural sorrow, loss, or pain,
That has been, and may be again?

Whate'er the theme, the Maiden sang
As if her song could have no ending;
I saw her singing at her work,
And o'er the sickle bending;—
I listen'd, motionless and still;
And, as I mounted up the hill,
The music in my heart I bore,
Long after it was heard no more.

William Wordsworth

from "SING A SONG OF JOY!"

Sing a song of joy!
Praise our God with mirth!
His flock who can destroy?
Is He not Lord of heaven and earth?

Sing we then secure,
Tuning well our strings!
With voice, as echo pure
Let us renown the King of Kings!

Thomas Campion

PSALM 100

Make a joyful noise unto the Lord, all ye lands.
Serve the Lord with gladness,
come before his presence with singing.
Know ye that the Lord he is God;
it is he that hath made us,
and not we ourselves;
we are his people,
and the sheep of his pasture.
Enter into his gates with thanksgiving,
and into his courts with praise;
be thankful unto him, and bless his name.
For the Lord is good,
his mercy is everlasting,
and his truth endureth to all generations.

OLD HUNDREDTH

Praise God from whom all blessings flow;
Praise Him, all creatures here below;
Praise Him above, ye heavenly host;
Praise Father, Son, and Holy Ghost.

Thomas Ken

OLD HUNDRED

The blacksmith did not hobble here
To the small church, on the hard hill,
In summer, to be told of stars;
He came with meek and tempered will;
He came, this hoarest of bent men,
To hear Old Hundred sung again.

But the young voice above the Book
Praised Him who built the heaven's fires;
And the old listener grew still;
No congregations and no choirs
Were in the grave with him at last;
Nothing but him and the sweet vast,

Nothing but those he soon must lose
If death was losing; and death was.
He saw them, wonderful and old,
But no power in them to pause
As they sailed on, as they sailed on,
Over his unmoving mound.

Mark Van Doren

THE VALLEY'S SINGING DAY

The sound of the closing outside door was all.
You made no sound in the grass with your footfall,
As far as you went from the door, which was not far;
But you had awakened under the morning star
The first song-bird that awakened all the rest.
He could have slept but a moment more at best.
Already determined dawn began to lay
In place across a cloud the slender ray
For prying beneath and forcing the lids of sight,
And loosing the pent-up music of over-night.
But dawn was not to begin their "pearly-pearly"
(By which they mean the rain is pearls so early,
Before it changes to diamonds in the sun),
Neither was song that day to be self-begun.
You had begun it, and if there needed proof—
I was asleep still under the dripping roof,
My window curtain hung over the sill to wet;
But I should awake to confirm your story yet;
I should be willing to say and help you say
That once you had opened the valley's singing day.

Robert Frost

THE SINGERS IN A CLOUD

Overhead at sunset all heard the choir.
Nothing could be seen except brighter grey
Raining beauty earthward, flooding with desire
All things that listened there in the broken day;
Songs from freer breathers, their unprisoned fire
Out of cloudy fountains, flying and hurled,
Fell and warmed the world.

Sudden came a wind and birds were laid bare,
Only music warmed them round their brown breasts.
They had sent the splendors pouring through the air,
Love was their heat and home far above their nests.
Light went softly out and left their voices there.
Starward passed for ever all that great cry,
Burning, round the sky.

On the earth the battles war against light,
Heavy lies the harrow, bitter the field.
Beauty, like a river running through the night,
Streams past the stricken ones whom it would have healed
But the darkened faces turn away from sight.
Blind, bewildered nations sow, reap, and fall,
Shadows gather all.

Far above the birdsong bright shines the gold,
Through the starry orchards earth's paths are hung;
As she moves among them glowing fruits unfold,
Such that the heavens there reawaken young.
Overhead is beauty, healing for the old
Overhead in morning, nothing but youth,
Only lovely youth.

Ridgely Torrence

AS I WENT SINGING OVER THE EARTH

As I went singing over the earth,
   Many a song I heard,
A song of death and a song of mirth,
A song that was of little worth,
   And the song of a bird.

Mary Coleridge

FOR THE EIGHTIETH BIRTHDAY
OF A GREAT SINGER

(*Sir George Henschel, b. 1850*)

When I was young I heard a tune
  From hills and forests far away,
Of maidens, youths and nightingales,
  Witches and woodland things at play.

Herr Walther sang it in his prime
  And down the years the echo sent
Till on the road to Sessenheim
  Young Wolfgang hummed it as he went.

Next Heine sang and Mörike
  And, for to take a wider air,
Schubert and Schumann, Löwe, Brahms—
  The magic called them, they were there!

Then from your lips we heard it rise,
  That old and ever youthful tune,
The full-lunged voice of sun-bright skies,
  Soft-breathed enchantment of the moon,

The miller dreaming by his wheel,
  The lover's sad or laughing mood,
The organ-grinder on the ice,
  The knight bewitched in the deep wood.

Which of your masks reveals you most,
    Reveals the old man's youthful eyes?
Surely the earliest of all,
    Hans Sachs, the kindly and the wise!

As he, so have you cherished well
    That ancient, lovely poetry,
And still, like his, your name recalls
    The perfume of the lilac-tree;

A piercing essence, sweet and wild,
    That wakes the heart to joy and tears
And now to us for evermore
    The essence of your eighty years.

Edward Shanks

THE SWAN AND GOOSE

A rich man bought a Swan and Goose—
That for song and this for use.
It chanced his simple-minded cook
One night the Swan for Goose mistook.
But in the dark about to chop
The Swan in two above the crop,
He heard the lyric note, and stayed
The action of the fatal blade.

And thus we see a proper tune
Is sometimes very opportune.

Aesop
Translated by William Ellery Leonard

THE DESIRED SWAN-SONG

Swans sing before they die—'twere no bad thing
Should certain persons die before they sing.

Samuel Taylor Coleridge

"THERE WAS AN OLD PERSON OF BRADLEY"

There was an old person of Bradley
Who sang all so loudly and sadly;
With a poker and tongs, He beat time to his songs,
That melodious old person of Bradley!

Edward Lear

OPERATIC NOTE

Apparently the Nibelungs
Were never cursed with feeble lungs.

Melville Cane

THE RAVEN

The gloom of death is on the raven's wing,
The song of death is in the raven's cries:
But when Demophilus begins to sing,
The raven dies.

Nicharchus
Translated by Edwin Arlington Robinson

61

BALLATA

of True and False Spring

A little wild bird sometimes at my ear
Sings his own little verses very clear:
Others sing louder that I do not hear.

For singing loudly is not singing well;
But ever by the song that's soft and low
The master-singer's voice is plain to tell.
Few have it, and yet all are masters now,
And each of them can trill out what he calls
His ballads, canzonets, and madrigals.

The world with masters is so covered o'er
There is no room for pupils any more.

Dante Gabriel Rossetti
Translation of an anonymous Italian poem

THE OVEN BIRD

There is a singer everyone has heard,
Loud, a mid-summer and a mid-wood bird,
Who makes the solid tree trunks sound again.
He says that leaves are old and that for flowers
Mid-summer is to spring as one to ten.
He says the early petal-fall is past
When pear and cherry bloom went down in showers
On sunny days a moment overcast;
And cones that other fall we name the fall.
He says the highway dust is over all.
The bird would cease and be as other birds
But that he knows in singing not to sing.
The question that he frames in all but words
Is what to make of a diminished thing.

Robert Frost

'ALLE VÖGEL SIND SCHON DA'

(Played by a Musical Box)

Are all the birds imprisoned there
Caught in that box of tinkling sound?
Birds from some fairy forest where
Their little ghosts move round and round.

Their bright breasts hidden in this cell
That holds the magic of a bird's
First morning song, the lovely swell
Of lifted notes that ask no words.

An air, perhaps, Scarlatti knew,
Or Mozart heard an angel sing,
As some enchanted blackbird flew
To herald an orchestral spring.

This secret life that hides within,
That joyous air, that happy store,
Held captive in this painted tin
For us, who now can sing no more.

Frances Chesterton

FOR M. S.
SINGING FRÜHLINGSGLAUBE IN 1945

Nun muss sich alles, alles wenden

Here are the Schubert Lieder. Now begin.

First the accompaniment,
Heart-known and heaven-sent
And so divinely right
The inmost spirit laughs with sure delight.

And now the fountain of the melody.

To your forgiven fields I am entered in,
Spring of my adolescence, Spring of the world,
Where every secret lime-leaf is unfurled,
Where all's made well again, yet more's to be—

Then why this misery?

Because, O enemy alien heart, we fear
That you are lost on your demoniac shore,
And we deny that in your music—here
Is your unchanged, unchanging innocent core.

Frances Cornford

"COME, LET US SOUND
WITH MELODY, THE PRAISES"

Come, let us sound with melody, the praises
Of the King's King, th' omnipotent Creator,
Author of number, that hath all the world in Harmony framed.

Thomas Campion

ONE GOD IS GOD OF BOTH

ONE GOD IS
GOD OF BOTH

Many poets, weary of wrestling with stubborn words, have envied—quite unrealistically—the composer who can express his ideas without encountering the tyranny of the alphabet. Musicians think otherwise and doubtless some of them wish they were free of the tyranny of the scale.

The affinity between poets and composers is not accidental. Poets, as well as composers, are often called music makers. There are certain composers who seem to have a special attraction for poets. Beethoven is chief of these and he has inspired a great number of poems, some of them of exceptional beauty and some extremely sentimental. Possibly such titles as the "Moonlight Sonata" and the "Sonata Appassionata" have been responsible for much heavy-handed verse though even Bach's austerity has not escaped the poetasters.

Poets have been interested in the forms of music as in other forms of art. Some poets, like Thomas Campion, have written both words and music; many more have written words for music as, of course, Shakespeare and Ben Jonson and Burns did.

Composers, in their turn, have set poetry to music as Beethoven did with Schiller's Ode to Joy *and as Benjamin Britten and Ralph Vaughan Williams are doing now. Sometimes composers write music suggested by poetry. Many poets have tried to do something more difficult and that is to write poems in the form of sonatas or even symphonies. Poems that have been written in musical forms are interesting as experiments, but they have not been successful experiments because these two arts, closely allied as they are, are not identical. Content must dictate form. The form of music is dictated by the structure and limitations of music. The form of poetry is dictated by the structure and limitations of language. Although great composers and great poets in every generation have pushed those boundaries back, they have not abolished them. Words cannot be used as notes are and, similarly, music cannot describe experience as language does. So-called "program" music needs many words to tell the audience what to expect. True music communicates its meaning without explanation for, indeed, as W. H. Auden says, "all others translate."*

The composers whom the poets have celebrated are not all known to us by name. Some, like the black and unknown bards of James Weldon Johnson's poem, have sung the tones "that helped make history when Time was young," others have been almost forgotten, save by the poets who have praised them.

THE COMPOSER

All the others translate: the painter sketches
A visible world to love or reject;
Rummaging into his living, the poet fetches
The images out that hurt and connect.

From Life to Art by painstaking adaption,
Relying on us to cover the rift;
Only your notes are pure contraption,
Only your song is an absolute gift.

Pour out your presence, O delight, cascading
The falls of the knee and the weirs of the spine,
Our climate of silence and doubt invading;

You alone, alone, O imaginary song,
Are unable to say an existence is wrong,
And pour out your forgiveness like a wine.

W. H. Auden

from A SONG TO DAVID

O Thou, that sit'st upon a throne,
With harp of high majestic tone,
  To praise the King of kings;
And voice of heav'n-ascending swell,
Which, while its deeper notes excell,
  Clear, as a clarion, rings:

    .   .   .   .   .

O Servant of God's holiest charge,
The minister of praise at large,
  Which thou may'st now receive;
From thy blest mansion hail and hear,
From topmost eminence appear
  To this the wreath I weave.

Christopher Smart

PROGRAM NOTE ON SIBELIUS

Between the pleasant lands, the sunlit places,
The meadows where the brooks are edged with mallow,
Abides the lurking void that leads the pensive
        Down to Avernus.

These are the darkened rooms, the unfrequented,
Where shriveled moths lie silent on the windows,
And treacherous doors conceal the unsuspected
        Terror to childhood.

All waning moons delay on far horizons
To taste familiar fears in groves forgotten,
The Druid trees where mistletoe and ivy
        Twine with the holm-oak.

And at the lonely door of Tuonela,
Singing the song of death that has no dying,
Still glides the swan across the mere of magic,
        Dark under cypress.

Donald Babcock

O BLACK AND UNKNOWN BARDS

O black and unknown bards of long ago,
How came your lips to touch the sacred fire?
How, in your darkness, did you come to know
The power and beauty of the minstrels' lyre?
Who first from midst his bonds lifted his eyes?
Who first from our the still watch, lone and long,
Feeling the ancient faith of prophets rise
Within his dark-kept soul, burst into song?

Heart of what slave poured out such melody
As "Steal away to Jesus"? On its strains
His spirit must have nightly floated free,
Though still about his hands he felt his chains.
Who heard great "Jordan roll"? Whose starward eye
Saw chariot "swing low"? And who was he
That breathed that comforting, melodic sigh,
"Nobody knows de trouble I see"?

What merely living clod, what captive thing,
Could up toward God through all its darkness grope,
And find within its deadened heart to sing
These songs of sorrow, love and faith, and hope?
How did it catch that subtle undertone,
That note in music heard not with the ears?
How sound the elusive reed so seldom blown
Which stirs the soul or melts the heart to tears.

74

Not that great German master in his dream
Of harmonies that thundered amongst the stars
At the creation, ever heard a theme
Nobler than "Go down, Moses." Mark its bars
How like a mighty trumpet-call they stir
The blood. Such are the notes that men have sung
Going to valorous deeds; such tones there were
That helped make history when Time was young.

There is a wide, wide wonder in it all,
That from degraded rest and servile toil
The fiery spirit of the seer should call
These simple children of the sun and soil.
O black slave singers, gone, forgot, unfamed,
You—you alone, of all the long, long line
Of those who've sung untaught, unknown, unnamed,
Have stretched out upward, seeking the divine.

You sang not deeds of heroes or of kings;
No chant of bloody war, no exulting paean
No arms-won triumphs; but your humble strings
You touched in chord with music empyrean.
You sang far better than you knew; the songs
That for your listeners' hungry hearts sufficed
Still live—but more than this to you belongs:
You sang a race from wood and stone to Christ.

James Weldon Johnson

PROPRIETY

Is some such word
   as the chord
      Brahms had heard
      from a bird,
sung down near the root of the throat;
it's the little downy woodpecker
            spiralling a tree—
            up up up like mercury:

   a not long
   sparrow-song
      of hayseed
      magnitude—
a tuned reticence with rigour
from strength at the source. Propriety is
            Bach's Solfegietto—
            harmonica and basso.

   The fish-spine
   on firs, on
      sombre trees
      by the sea's
walls of wave-worn rock—have it; and
a moonbow and Bach's cheerful firmness
            in a minor key.
            It's an owl-and-a-pussy-

76

both-content
agreement.
    Come, come. It's
    mixed with wits;
it's not a graceful sadness. It's
resistance with bent head, like foxtail
    millet's. Brahms and Bach,
    no; Bach and Brahms. To thank Bach

for his song
first, is wrong.
    Pardon me;
    both are the
unintentional pansy-face
uncursed by self-inspection; blackened
    because born that way.

Marianne Moore

EPIGRAM ON HANDEL AND BONONCINI

Some say, compar'd to *Bononcini*
That Mynheer *Handel's* but a Ninny;
Others aver, that he to *Handel*
Is scarcely fit to hold a *Candle*.
Strange all this Difference should be
'Twixt Tweedle-*dum* and Tweedle-*dee!*

John Byrom

ON THE DEATH OF MR. PURCELL

I

Mark how the Lark and Linnet Sing,
      With rival Notes
   They strain their warbling Throats,
    To welcome in the Spring.
    But in the close of Night,
When *Philomel* begins her Heav'nly Lay,
    They cease their mutual spight,
    Drink in her Musick with delight,
And list'ning and silent, and silent and list'ning, and list'ning
                     and silent obey.

II

So ceas'd the rival Crew when *Purcell* came
They Sung no more, or only Sung his Fame.
    Struck dumb they all admir'd
      The God-like Man,
    Alas, too soon retir'd,
      As He too late began.
We beg not Hell our *Orpheus* to restore,
      Had He been there,
      Their Sovereign's fear
    Had sent Him back before.
The pow'r of Harmony too well they knew,
He long e'er this had Tun'd their jarring Sphere,
    And left no Hell below.

The Heav'nly Quire, who heard his Notes from high,
Let down the Scale of Musick from the Sky:
   They handed him along,
And all the way He taught, and all the way they Sung.
Ye Brethren of the *Lyre* and tunefull Voice,
Lament his lott: but at your own rejoyce.
Now live secure and linger out your days,
The Gods are pleas'd alone with *Purcell's Layes,*
   Nor know to mend their Choice.

John Dryden

AN EPITAPH UPON THE CELEBRATED CLAUDY PHILIPS, MUSICIAN, WHO DIED VERY POOR

Philips, whose touch harmonious could remove
The pangs of guilty pow'r and hapless love,
Rest here, distress'd by poverty no more,
Here find that calm, thou gav'st so oft before.
Sleep, undisturb'd, within this peaceful shrine,
Till angels wake thee, with a note like thine.

Samuel Johnson

HENRY PURCELL

The poet wishes well to the divine genius of Purcell and praises him that, whereas other musicians have given utterance to the moods of man's mind, he has, beyond that, uttered in notes the very make and species of man as created both in him and in all men generally.

Have fair fallen, O fair, fair have fallen, so dear
To me, so arch-especial a spirit as heaves in Henry Purcell,
An age is now since passed, since parted; with the reversal
Of the outward sentence low lays him, listed to a heresy, here.

Not mood in him nor meaning, proud fire or sacred fear,
Or love or pity or all that sweet notes not his might nursle:
It is the forgèd feature finds me; it is the rehearsal
Of own, of abrúpt sélf there so thrusts on, so throngs the ear.

Let him oh! with his air of angels then lift me, lay me! only I'll
Have an eye to the sakes of him, quaint moonmarks, to his pelted
    plumage under
Wings: so some great stormfowl, whenever he has walked his
    while

The thunder-purple seabeach plumèd purple-of-thunder,
If a wuthering of his palmy snow-pinions scatter a colossal smile
Off him, but meaning motion fans fresh our wits with wonder.

Gerard Manley Hopkins

MOZART PERHAPS

Walking at night alone,
I heard, in a house on a dune along the shore,
The tinkle of a piano idly played—
Mozart perhaps, the music Man has made—
The little intricate tune
Spelled out its human pathos tenderly
Against the oceanic surge and roar,
The barbarous choiring of the wind and sea,
That here shall sound when Man is here no more,
His plaintive music gone—
While they rave on.

John Hall Wheelock

SHELDONIAN SOLILOQUY

(*During Bach's B Minor Mass*)

My music-loving Self this afternoon
(Clothed in the gilded surname of Sassoon)
Squats in the packed Sheldonian and observes
An intellectual bee-hive perched and seated
in Achromatic and expectant curves
Of buzzing, sunbeam-flecked, and overheated
Accommodation. Skins perspire . . . But hark! . . .
Begins the great *B minor Mass* of Bach.

The choir sings *Gloria in excelsis Deo*
With confident and well-conducted *brio*.
Outside, a motor-bike makes impious clatter,
Impinging on our Eighteenth-Century trammels.
God's periwigged: He takes a pinch of snuff.
The music's half-rococo. . . . Does it matter
While those intense musicians shout the stuff
In Catholic Latin to the cultured mammals
Who agitate the pages of their scores? . . .

Meanwhile, in Oxford sunshine out of doors,
Birds in collegiate gardens rhapsodize
Antediluvian airs of worm-thanksgiving.
To them the austere and buried Bach replies
With song that from ecclesiasmus cries

Eternal *Resurrexit* to the living.
Hosanna in excelsis chants the choir
In pious contrapuntal jubilee.
Hosanna shrill the birds in sunset fire.
And Benedictus sings my heart to Me.

Siegfried Sassoon

EUTYCHIDES

Eutychides, who wrote the songs,
Is going down where he belongs.
O you unhappy ones, beware:
Eutychides will soon be there!
For he is coming with twelve lyres,
And with more than twice twelve quires
Of the stuff that he has done
In the world from which he's gone.
Ah, now must you know death indeed,
For he is coming with all speed;
And with Eutychides in Hell,
Where's a poor tortured soul to dwell?

Lucilius
Translated by Edwin Arlington Robinson

MOZART, 1935

Poet, be seated at the piano.
Play the present, its hoo-hoo-hoo,
Its shoo-shoo-shoo, its ric-a-nic,
Its envious cachinnation.

If they throw stones upon the roof
While you practice arpeggios,
It is because they carry down the stairs
A body in rags.
Be seated at the piano.

That lucid souvenir of the past,
The divertimento;
That airy dream of the future,
The unclouded concerto . . .
The snow is falling.
Strike the piercing chord.

Be thou the voice,
Not you. Be thou, be thou
The voice of angry fear,
The voice of this besieging pain.

Be thou that wintry sound
As of the great wind howling,
By which sorrow is released,

Dismissed, absolved
In a starry placating.

We may return to Mozart
He was young, and we, we are old.
The snow is falling
And the streets are full of cries.
Be seated, thou.

Wallace Stevens

ON HEARING A SYMPHONY
OF BEETHOVEN

Sweet sounds, oh, beautiful music, do not cease!
Reject me not into the world again.
With you alone is excellence and peace,
Mankind made plausible, his purpose plain.
Enchanted in your air benign and shrewd,
With limbs a-sprawl and empty faces pale,
The spiteful and the stingy and the rude
Sleep like the scullions in the fairy-tale.
This moment is the best the world can give:
The tranquil blossom on the tortured stem.
Reject me not, sweet sounds! oh, let me live,
Till Doom espy my towers and scatter them,
A city spell-bound under the aging sun,
Music my rampart, and my only one.

Edna St. Vincent Millay

BEETHOVEN'S DEATH MASK

I imagine him still with heavy brow.
Huge, black, with bent head and falling hair
He ploughs the landscape. His face
Is this hanging mask transfigured,
This mask of death which the white lights make stare.

I see the thick hands clasped; the scare-crow coat;
The light strike upwards at the holes for eyes;
The beast squat in that mouth, whose opening is
The hollow opening of an organ pipe:
There the wind sings and the harsh longing cries.

He moves across my vision like a ship.
What else is iron but he? The fields divide
And, heaving, are changing waters of the sea.
He is prisoned, masked, shut off from being.
Life, like a fountain, he sees leap—outside.

Yet, in that head there twists the roaring cloud
And coils, as in a shell, the roaring wave.
The damp leaves whisper; bending to the rain
The April rises in him, chokes his lungs
And climbs the torturing passage of his brain.

Then the drums move away, the Distance shows;
Now cloud-hid peaks are bared; the mystic One
Horizons haze, as the blue incense, heaven.
Peace, peace. . . . Then splitting skull and dream, there come
Blotting our lights, the Trumpeter, the sun.

Stephen Spender

from IVES

This is Charles Ives.
He gathers the known world total into music,
passion of sense, perspective's mask of light
into suggestion's inarticulate
gesture, invention. Knowing the voices, knowing
these faces and music and this breeding landscape
balanced between the crisis and the cold
which bears the many-born, he parcels silence
into a music which submerges prayer,
rising as rivers of faces overhead,
naming the instruments we all must hold.

Muriel Rukeyser

PIPING DOWN THE VALLEYS WILD

Piping down the valleys wild,
Piping songs of pleasant glee,
On a cloud I saw a child,
And he laughing said to me:

'Pipe a song about a Lamb!'
So I piped with merry cheer.
'Piper, pipe that song again;'
So I piped: he wept to hear.

'Drop thy pipe, thy happy pipe;
Sing thy songs of happy cheer:
So I sang the same again,
While he wept with joy to hear.

'Piper, sit thee down and write
In a book, that all may read.'
So he vanish'd from my sight,
And I pluck'd a hollow reed,

And I made a rural pen,
And I stain'd the water clear,
And I wrote my happy songs
Every child may joy to hear.

William Blake

BARTHÉLÉMON AT VAUXHALL

François Hippolite Barthélémon, first-fiddler at Vauxhall Gardens, composed what was probably the most popular morning hymn-tune ever written. It was formerly sung, full-voiced, every Sunday in most churches, to Bishop Ken's words, but is now seldom heard.

He said: "Awake my soul, and with the sun," . . .
And paused upon the bridge, his eyes due east,
Where was emerging like a full-robed priest
The irradiate globe that vouched the dark as done.

It lit his face—the weary face of one
Who in the adjacent gardens charged his string,
Nightly, with many a tuneful tender thing,
Till stars were weak, and dancing hours outrun.

And then were threads of matin music spun
In trial tones as he pursued his way:
"This is a morn," he murmured, "well begun:
This strain to Ken will count when I am clay!"

And count it did; till, caught by echoing lyres,
It spread to galleried naves and mighty quires.

Thomas Hardy

THE WEARY BLUES

Droning a drowsy syncopated tune,
Rocking back and forth to a mellow croon,
    I heard a Negro play.
Down on Lenox Avenue the other night
By the pale dull pallor of an old gas light
    He did a lazy sway. . . .
    He did a lazy sway. . . .
To the tune o' those Weary Blues.
With his ebony hands on each ivory key
He made that poor piano moan with melody.
    O Blues!
Swaying to and fro on his rickety stool
He played that sad raggy tune like a musical fool.
    Sweet Blues!
Coming from a black man's soul.
    O Blues!
In a deep song voice with a melancholy tone
I heard that Negro sing, that old piano moan—
    "Ain't got nobody in all this world,
    Ain't got nobody but maself.
    I's gwine to quit ma frownin'
    And put ma troubles on the shelf."
Thump, thump, thump, went his foot on the floor.
He played a few chords then he sang some more—
    "I got the Weary Blues
    And I can't be satisfied.

Got the Weary Blues
And can't be satisfied—
I ain't happy no mo'
And I wish that I had died."
And far into the night he crooned that tune.
The stars went out and so did the moon.
The singer stopped playing and went to bed
While the Weary Blues echoed through his head.
He slept like a rock or a man that's dead.

Langston Hughes

from THE CARNIVAL OF ANIMALS

INTRODUCTION

Camille St. Saëns was racked with pains
When people addressed him as "Saint Sains."
He held the human race to blame
Because it could not pronounce his name.
So he turned with metronome and fife
To glorify other forms of life.
Be quiet, please, for here begins
His salute to feathers, furs, and fins.

THE BIRDS

Puccini was Latin, and Wagner Teutonic,
And birds are incurably philharmonic.
Suburban yards and rural vistas
Are filled with avian Andrews Sisters.
The skylark sings a roundelay,
The crow sings The Road To Mandalay.
The nightingale sings a lullaby
And the seagull sings a gullaby.
That's what shepherds listened to in Arcadia
Before someone invented the radia.

Ogden Nash

IBERIA

Oh, Spanish composers may seem quite *castizo*
And spend their whole lives in trying to be so—
Sing *cante hondo,* drink wine from the *bota,*
Touch the guitar, and dance the *jota,*

But French composers sit in cafés,
Sipping absinthe, and wearing berets,
And, as soon as they start feeling no pain,
Write, *in absentia,* the music of Spain.

Although Debussy never visited Spain, his Iberia *is more Spanish than any Spanish music that has ever been written by her countrymen.*
                                        —George Copeland in the *Atlantic*

Leo Kirschenbaum

ON A PIECE OF MUSIC

How all's to one thing wrought!
The members, how they sit!
O what a tune the thought
Must be that fancied it.

Nor angel insight can
Learn how the heart is hence:
Since all the make of man
Is law's indifference.

What makes the man and what
The man within that makes:
Ask whom he serves or not
Serves and what side he takes.

For good grows wild and wide,
Has shades, is nowhere none;
But right must seek a side
And choose for chieftain one.

Who built these walls made known
The music of his mind,
Yet here he had but shewn
His ruder-rounded rind.

Not free in this because
His powers seemed free to play:
He swept what scope he was
To sweep and must obey.

Though down his being's bent
Like air he changed in choice,
That was an instrument
Which overvaulted voice.

Therefore this masterhood,
This piece of perfect song,
This fault-not-found-with good,
Is neither right nor wrong.

No more than red and blue,
No more than Re and Mi,
Or sweet the golden glue
That's built for by the bee.

Gerard Manley Hopkins

ON FIRST HEARING BEETHOVEN

Whose absolute dumbness circumscribed by sound
Dumbfounds and profoundly confounds the boundary
Of my sense, I hear, in dense silence founded
By supernal sound, the immense harmonic like mountains
Intensely imbedded in man in agony bound and drowned.

Upon pristine infinity limits first drawn
Encircling the sky establishing distance in stars
Like records, or installing sight, touch, hearing; thus
My mind seeks, feels, states, herewith I am donated
A sixth terrible sense, measurement of pain of sorrow.

Beyond this being I and being not that mind
That blind to its kind finds in the divine its kind,
Being but I, I cry to these signs I am confined
May vainly try to divine deeper the upward mine
Driven through abysmal heaven, but having yet to die

Deaf dumb and blind can only stare at the sky.

George Barker

POET TO DANCER

POET
TO DANCER

Just as poets have written of the music of the spheres they have
written of the dancing of the spheres and the dancing of the seas.
The rhythm of the universe, like the rhythm of our pulses,
determines the rhythm of the dance. Apollo, the god of music,
was the god of the dance as well. In Greek drama, the chorus
commented on the action of the play through both song and
dance.

A charming old carol called "Tomorrow Shall Be My Dancing
Day," preserves some of the atmosphere of the time when our word
"carol" which now means a song, meant a dance, and when
dances were a part of Christian ritual. David danced before the
Ark, we know, and many sects in both the Jewish and Christian
religions have used dancing in their worship, as some Eastern
religions still do. Many of the poems in this section have to do
with the essentially religious nature of the dance. Modern poets
are as concerned with this as were the older poets.

Dancing as performance is relatively new in the world's history.
Ballet, though descended from the pantomime of ancient Rome,

was perfected as entertainment in the seventeenth century, only three hundred years ago. Ballet and ballad derive from the same Latin root, ballare—to dance, just as chorus and carol derive from the same Greek root, choros—a dance, plus aulos—a flute. The close relationship of music, poetry, and the dance extends even to the words which pertain to each.

The dance, existing as it does in both time and space, has kindled the imagination of many poets who see in the dance a way to unite the arts of seeing and the arts of hearing. Grace and seriousness and joy are the essence of the dance; dancers and poets understand this and speak to each other as they may.

61993

THE DANCER AT CRUACHAN
AND CRO-PATRICK

I, proclaiming that there is
Among birds or beasts or men
One that is perfect or at peace,
Danced on Cruachan's windy plain,
Upon Cro-Patrick sang aloud;
All that could run or leap or swim
Whether in wood, water or cloud,
Acclaiming, proclaiming, declaiming Him.

W. B. Yeats

from SONNETS TO ORPHEUS
Second Part

Oh, come and go, you almost child, entrancing
for one brief hour the figure of the dance
to purest constellation of the dancing
where, subject as we are to change and chance,

we beat dull nature. For she only started
hearing with all her ears at Orpheus' song.
And you still moved with motion then imparted
and shrank a little when a tree seemed long

On treading with you the remembered pace.
You knew it still, that passage where the lyre
soundingly rose, the unimagined centre,

and practiced all your steps in hope to enter
that theme again, whirling to one entire
communion with your friend both feet and face.

Rainer Maria Rilke
Translated by J. B. Leishman

101

from THE POWER OF MUSIC

O lyre of gold, Apollo's
Treasure, shared with the violet-wreathed Muses,
The light foot hears you, and the brightness begins:
Your notes compel the singer
When to lead out the dance
The prelude is sounded·on your trembling strings.
You quench the warrior Thunderbolt's everlasting flame:
On God's sceptre the Eagle sleeps,
Drooping his swift wings on either side.

Pindar
Translated by H. T. Wade-Gery and C. M. Bowra

from THE WINTER'S TALE

When you sing,
I'd have you buy and sell so, so give alms,
Pray so; and for the ord'ring your affairs,
To sing them too. When you do dance, I wish you
A wave o' the sea, that you might ever do
Nothing but that; move still, still so,
And own no other function.

William Shakespeare

102

from ORCHESTRA

'Or from what spring doth your opinion rise,
      That dancing is a frenzy and a rage,
      First known and used in this new-fangled age?

'Dancing, bright lady, then began to be,
    When the first seeds whereof the world did spring,
The fire, air, earth, and water, did agree
    By Love's persuasion, nature's mighty king,
    To leave their first discorded combating,
      And in a dance such measure to observe,
      As all the world their motion should preserve.

'Since when they still are carried in a round,
    And changing come one in another's place;
Yet do they neither mingle nor confound,
    But every one doth keep the bounded space
    Wherein the dance doth bid it turn or trace.
      This wondrous miracle did Love devise,
      For dancing is love's proper exercise.'

Sir John Davies

from FOUR FOR SIR JOHN DAVIES

THE DANCE

Is that dance slowing in the mind of man
That made him think the universe could hum?
The great wheel turns its axle when it can;
I need a place to sing, and dancing-room,
And I have made a promise to my ears
I'll sing and whistle romping with the bears.

For they are all my friends: I saw one slide
Down a steep hillside on a cake of ice,—
Or was that in a book? I think with pride:
A caged bear rarely does the same thing twice
In the same way: O watch his body sway!—
This animal remembering to be gay.

I tried to fling my shadow at the moon,
The while my blood leaped with a wordless song.
Though dancing needs a master, I had none
To teach my toes, to listen to my tongue.
But what I learned there, dancing all alone,
Was not the joyless motion of a stone.

I take this cadence from a man named Yeats;
I take it, and I give it back again:
For other tunes and other wanton beats
Have tossed my heart and fiddled through my brain.
Yes, I was dancing-mad, and how
That came to be the bears and Yeats would know.

Theodore Roethke

104

from A SONG OF DAGGER-DANCING

There lived years ago the beautiful Kung-sun,
Who, dancing with her dagger, drew from all four quarters
An audience like mountains lost among themselves.
Heaven and earth moved back and forth, following her motions,
Which were bright as when the Archer shot the nine suns down the
    sky
And rapid as angels before the wings of dragons.
She began like a thunderbolt, venting its anger,
And ended like the shining calm of rivers and the sea.

Tu Fu
Translated by Witter Bynner

WALTZING IT

Never talk to me of waltzing it,
    Giddily, O! Giddily, O!
'Tis a dance has many faults in it,
    Giddily, O! Giddily, O!
First it strains our stays, in a thousand ways,
    Whiskers much amaze, till your collar strays,
And you make a thousand halts in it,
    Giddily, Giddily, O!

William Thomas Moncrieff

SUPERLATIVE DANCE AND SONG

Shake off your heavy trance,
    And leap into a dance
Such as no mortals use to tread,
    Fit only for Apollo
To play to, for the moon to lead
    And all the stars to follow.

O blessed youths, for Jove doth pause,
Laying aside his graver laws
    For this device;
And at the wedding such a pair
Each dance is taken for a prayer,
    Each song a sacrifice.

Francis Beaumont

106

HARP MUSIC—

"Softly, let—"

(The alternate stanzas in old Welsh meters,
Awdl gywydd, and Cywydd deuair hirion, respectively.)

Softly, let the measure break
Till the dancers wake, and rise,
Lace their golden shoes, and turn
Toward the stars that burn their eyes.

Softly, let the measure flow,
Float in silver, and follow.

Softly, let the measure dwell
Slowly, as the spell is wound
Out and in, through space and time,
While the sandals rhyme the round.

Softly, let the measure stir,
Lift, subside, and go under.

Softly, let the measure prove
The bright cadence moving there
Changing, for unbroken dark,
The illumined arc of air.

Softly, let the measure be
Unheard, but never wholly.

Rolfe Humphries

from WHERE SHALL WISDOM
BE FOUND?

Will they ever come to me, ever again,
   The long long dances,
On through the dark till the dawn-stars wane?
Shall I feel the dew on my throat, and the stream
Of wind in my hair? Shall our white feet gleam
   In the dim expanses?

Euripides (from THE BACCHAE)
Translated by Gilbert Murray

BURGUNDIAN CAROL

Patapan

Willie, take your little drum,
With your whistle, Robin, come!
   When we hear the fife and drum,
Ture-lure-lu, pata-pata-pan,
    When we hear the fife and drum,
    Christmas should be frolicsome.

Thus the men of olden days
Loved the King of kings to praise:
   When they hear the fife and drum,
Ture-lure-lu, pata-pata-pan,
    When they hear the fife and drum
    Sure our children won't be dumb!

God and man are now become
More at one than fife and drum
   When you hear the fife and drum
Ture-lure-lu, pata-pata-pan,
    When you hear the fife and drum
    Dance, and make the village hum!

Bernard de la Monnoye
Translated by Percy Dearmer

109

from LOVE RESTORED

This motion was of Love begot,
  It was so airy, light, and good
His wings into their feet he shot,
  Or else himself into their blood.
But ask not how. The end will prove
That love's in them, or they're in love.

Have men beheld the Graces dance,
  Or seen the upper orbs to move?
So these did turn, return, advance,
  Drawn back by Doubt, put on by Love.
And now, like earth, themselves they fix
Till greater powers vouchsafe to mix
  Their motions with them. Do not fear,
  You brighter planets of this sphere:
    Not one male heart you see
      But rather to his female eyes
      Would die a destin'd sacrifice
    Than live at home and free.

Ben Jonson

110

VAUDEVILLE DANCER

When, to a cheap and tawdry tune, the orchestra cried out,
Frantic, in violent syncopation, you began
With slender, imperious body in mournful grace to move about
Through the old devious patterns, the device of man.

How suddenly then, silent magnificence, you put to shame
The crowded and garish theatre, the strangled cries
Of flute and trumpet—O mortal body, bearer of our flame
Through the drear lands of death, guardian of the mysteries!

Revered, reviled, wept and adored, besought, cried out upon
By hungering lips of the ages—the sacred source of things,
That glimmered in Thrace, that shone in Rome, that swayed in
    Babylon,
Here moves to the vile throb of castanets and strings.

Oh, through what generations have you lured, what secret ways,
Man's fainting heart to be reborn—what splendors move
Deep in his breast when, dolorous, your reluctant beauty sways
In the old weary rhythms of unwearied love!

John Hall Wheelock

THE FIDDLER OF DOONEY

When I play on my fiddle in Dooney,
Folk dance like a wave of the sea;
My cousin is priest in Kilvarnet,
My brother in Mocharabuiee.

I passed my brother and cousin:
They read in their books of prayer;
I read in my book of songs
I bought at the Sligo fair.

When we come at the end of time
To Peter sitting in state,
He will smile on the three old spirits,
But call me first through the gate;

For the good are always the merry,
Save by an evil chance,
And the merry love the fiddle,
And the merry love to dance:

And when the folk there spy me,
They will all come up to me,
With 'Here is the fiddler of Dooney!'
And dance like a wave of the sea.

William Butler Yeats

PEDIMENT: BALLET

Music can not stay
But there's a way
To fix and save
Its flowing—
By marbled motion in a frieze,
In eave above the architrave,
Of figures poising and at ease
With discs for throwing.

But here, today,
Marble to music comes again,
Statues to men. . . .
These dancers have been brave
Beyond their knowing.
For men to pose
As statues at their play
Is strangely far more beautiful,
More strong to pull
The cord of terror taut,
Than that a statue can
Be like a man.

Why?
What does it signify?
And no one knows.
This sculpture lives:

The discus thrower really throws.
The flying javelin is caught
But not before it gives,
In unaccounted ways,
A wound which will not mend.

Marble to music come again,
Statues to men,
And statues' shadows moving . . .
Proving
That all is music in the end
And only music stays.

Louise Townsend Nicholl

I CANNOT DANCE UPON MY TOES

I cannot dance upon my toes,
No man instructed me,
But often times among my mind
A glee possesseth me
That had I ballet knowledge
Would put itself abroad
In pirouette to blanch a troupe,
Or lay a Prima mad!
And though I had no gown of gauze,
No ringlet to my hair,
Nor hopped for audiences like birds,
One claw upon the air,—
Nor tossed my shape in eider balls
Nor rolled on wheels of snow
Till I was out of sight in sound,
The house encored me so—
Nor any knew I know the art
I mention easy here—
Nor any placard boast me,
It's full as opera!

Emily Dickinson

TO POTAPOVITCH

(*of the Ballet Russe*)

Vault on the opal carpet of the sun,
Barbaric Prince Igor:—or, blind Pierrot,
Despair until the moon by tears be won;—
Or, Daphnis, move among the bees with Chloe.

Release,—dismiss the passion from your arms.
More real than life, the gestures you have spun
Haunt the blank stage with lingering alarms,
Though silent as your sandals, danced undone.

Hart Crane

THE SWAN

The trumpets were curled away, the drum beat no more,
Only the Swan, the Swan, danced in my brain:
All night she spun; dropped, lifted again,
Arched and curved her arms; sunk on the frore
Snow-brittle feathers skirting her; reclined on hands
Buckling her waist, where the moon glanced.
How small her waist was, and the feet that danced!

Sometimes she bent back, and a breeze fanned
Her hair that touched the ground, and, shown
Between her Swan's legs, feathers and white down.

Stephen Spender

from ELEGY ON THE DEATH OF MME. ANNA PAVLOVA

The glory and the ardour of the stage,
The dazzling feet that made a mock of death,
The exultation, the delicious rage,
Are cast upon the chilly morning's breath.

. . . . .

In her we saw the Being, not the bird,
The rapture of a Spirit uncreate;
Less in the flutes than in those feet we heard
The pride that lifts men far above their fate.

E. H. W. Meyerstein

HOMAGE TO VASLAV NIJINSKY

You are that legendary figure, never seen,
   but always glimpsed beyond the dim
dream's transparent backcloth; or in green,
   dark groves, the wings of time's topless auditorium,
there where at evening the misted lake is laid away
like a remembered silence in the angry day
   you wander, a young and lonely prince,
far from the huntsmen in the magic wood,
   and drawn by sinister enchantments, visions
of a swan that glides and calls across the haunted glade.

You are the rose breathing its own and universal essence,
   the shadow leaping from the body it has understood
into music's air, the pure design of its deliverance
   and pattern of the mind's bare, ordered solitude.
You are both fool and harlequin, the gay and melancholy
dancer at funerals of innocence and love's wise folly.
   You are the loveless, lost, the lonely and the dumb,
the vanquished who alone rehearse what triumphs mean,
   the spectre whose reality is our belief; the faun for whom
no curtain falls upon the mystery that he has always known.

James Kirkup

FOR NIJINSKY'S TOMB

Nijinsky's ashes here in peace repose
No more the Faun, the Harlequin, the Rose.

We saw him framed in light before the crowds,
Hushed like a tree that waits the touch of dawn,
A panther ready, or an arrow drawn.
Then music came, the sure, awakening bars,
He leapt beyond the bounds of joy and grief;
His heart conferred in those transfigured hours,
Strength like the sun, precision like the stars;
The sea was his; the buoyancy of clouds,
The sap that flows in every fluted leaf,
The blossoming, in light, of fields of flowers.
Yet later, smiling in applauded grace,
The Faun, the Rose was never wholly ours,
We saw remoteness in the tilted face,
He heard alone, beyond our human ears,
Beyond applause, the Music of the Spheres.

Nijinsky's ashes here in peace are laid
Their perfect tribute to Perfection paid.

Frances Cornford

POET TO DANCER

Moving with you
I dare
leap up
the curving stair of space
to lay a lucid meaning
on the air
and trace
an arc of language,
as a heart-beat
loud and bare;

only in love beside
or hate
can ebb and flow of flesh
so plain articulate,
can breast and palm and thigh
dazzling as wing of humming bird
out-cry.

o, could the word
so speak,
reply,
be heard!

Bernice Kavinoky

122

MUSIC SHALL UNTUNE THE SKY

MUSIC SHALL
UNTUNE THE SKY

*Whatever the structure of our world, music has a place in it,
whether as part of a Divine Plan or as the purest of man's inventions. John Dryden, in his most beautiful and most familiar poem,
"A Song for St. Cecilia's Day," "From harmony, from heavenly
harmony, this universal frame began," expresses with unequaled
felicity the thought that music is the force that created our universe. So pervasive is the power of music and the power of this
poem that a modern poet, George Barker, has written an "Ode
Against St. Cecilia's Day," a despairing song of war and death,
in which he calls on the seas to mourn "Till Cecilia turns to a
stone."*

*Poets still write as though the sun and the planets whirl about in
the measures of the dance or the measures of music. John Hall
Wheelock calls this rhythm the "iron governance." Even scientists
speak of the dance of the atoms, knowing that this figure of
speech will convey their meaning with economy and precision.
Music and dancing appear everywhere in nature and, though
modern poets no longer ask why birds sing or why the stars
dance, the questions remain.*

The power of music is not always a cosmic power. Music may be as simple as a children's song or as compelling as a bugle, as lonesome as the blues, or as gay as a country dance. All these aspects of music have been explored by poets all over the world. Chinese music, Hebrew music, Greek music, all sound strange to us, yet Chinese, Hebrew, and Greek poets have found in their music the emotions that are common to us all. Poets everywhere write of the music of exile, music of praise and of sorrow, of love and of childhood, all universal themes. Music calls forth a response in all of us; poets distill their emotions into words so that reader and poet share an experience. Yet poets, paradoxically, are keenly aware of the limitations of words; they know that only music can reach beyond words. In these poems, poets have celebrated the power of music and, beyond music, the power of silence, for silence too is a part of music.

The greatest of our poets have heard in music the "full-fugued song of the universe unending," as Hardy did, and have made us hear that song too. The trumpets sound on the other side. The echoes reach us here.

from THE MAN WITH THE BLUE GUITAR

I

The man bent over his guitar,
A shearsman of sorts. The day was green.

They said, "You have a blue guitar,
You do not play things as they are."

The man replied, "Things as they are
Are changed upon the blue guitar."

And they said then, "But play, you must,
A tune beyond us, yet ourselves,

A tune upon the blue guitar
Of things exactly as they are."

II

I cannot bring a world quite round,
Although I patch it as I can.

I sing a hero's head, large eye
And bearded bronze, but not a man,

Although I patch him as I can
And reach through him almost to man.

126

If to serenade almost to man
Is to miss, by that, things as they are,

Say that it is the serenade
Of a man that plays a blue guitar.

Wallace Stevens

from HYMNE TO GOD MY GOD,
IN MY SICKNESSE

Since I am comming to that Holy roome,
   Where, with thy Quire of Saints for evermore,
I shall be made thy Musique; As I come
   I tune the Instrument here at the dore,
   And what I must doe then, thinke here before.

John Donne

HEARING THE EARLY ORIOLE

(*Written in exile*)

When the sun rose I was still lying in bed;
An early oriole sang on the roof of my house.
For a moment I thought of the Royal Park at dawn
When the Birds of Spring greeted their Lord from his trees.
I remembered the days when I served before the Throne
Pencil in hand, on duty at the Ch'ēng-ming;
At the height of spring when I paused an instant from work,
Morning and evening, was *this* the voice I heard?
Now in my exile the oriole sings again
In the dreary stillness of Hsün-yang town . . .
The bird's note cannot really have changed;
All the difference lies in the listener's heart.
If he could but forget that he lives at the World's end,
The bird would sing as it sang in the Palace of old.

Po Chü-i
Translated by Arthur Waley

TO HEAR AN ORIOLE SING

To hear an oriole sing
May be a common thing,
Or only a divine.

It is not of the bird
Who sings the same, unheard,
As unto crowd.

The fashion of the ear
Attireth that it hear
In dun or fair.

So whether it be rune,
Or whether it be none.
Is of within;

The "tune is in the tree,"
The sceptic showeth me;
"No, sir! In thee!"

Emily Dickinson

"CAN DOLEFUL NOTES
TO MESUR'D ACCENTS SET"

Can doleful notes to mesur'd accents set
Express unmesur'd Griefs which Time forget?
No, let Chromatick Tunes, harsh without ground,
Be sullen music for a tuneless Heart.
Chromatick Tunes most like my passions sound,
And if combined to bear their falling part,
Uncertain certain turns, of thoughts forecast,
Bring back the same, then dye and dying last.

John Danyel

from THE TEMPEST

Where should this music be? I' the air, or the earth?
It sounds no more; and sure, it waits upon
Some god o' the island. Sitting on a bank,
Weeping again the king my father's wreck,
This music crept by me upon the waters,
Allaying both their fury and my passion
With its sweet air.

William Shakespeare

130

from AT A SOLEMN MUSICK

Blest pair of Sirens, pledges of Heaven's joy,
Sphere-born harmonious Sisters, Voice and Vers,
Wed your divine sounds, and mixt power employ
Dead things with inbreath'd sense able to pierce,
And to our high-rais'd phantasie present,
That undisturbèd Song of pure concent,
Ay sung before the sapphire-colour'd throne
To him that sits theron
With Saintly shout, and solemn Jubily,
Where the bright Seraphim in burning row
Their loud up-lifted Angel trumpets blow,
And the Cherubick host in thousand quires
Touch their immortal Harps of golden wires,
With those just Spirits that wear victorious Palms,
Hymns devout and holy Psalms
Singing everlastingly;
That we on Earth with undiscording voice
May rightly answer that melodious noise. . . .

John Milton

131

from FLUTE-PRIEST SONG FOR RAIN

Whistle under the water,
Make the water bubble to the tones of the flute.
I call the bluebird's song into the water:
Wee-kee! Wee-kee-kee!
Dawn is coming,
The morning star shines upon us.
Bluebird singing to the West clouds,
Bring the humming rain

Water-rattles shake,
Flute whistles,
Star in Heaven shines.
I blow the oriole's song,
The yellow song of the North.
I call rain-clouds with my rattles:
Wee-kee-kee, oriole,
Pattering rain.

Amy Lowell

IN A MUSEUM

I

Here's the mould of a musical bird long passed from light,
Which over the earth before man came was winging;
There's a contralto voice I heard last night,
That lodges in me still with its sweet singing.

II

Such a dream is Time that the coo of this ancient bird
Has perished not, but is blent, or will be blending
Mid visionless wilds of space with the voice that I heard,
In the full-fugued song of the universe unending.

Thomas Hardy

"TO MUSIC BENT IS MY RETIRED MIND"

To music bent, is my retired mind,
And fain would I some song of pleasure sing,
But in vain joys no comfort now I find;
From heavenly thoughts all true delight doth spring.
Thy power, Oh God, thy mercies, to record,
Will sweeten every note and every word.

All earthly pomp or beauty to express,
Is but to carve in snow, on waves to write.
Celestial things, though men conceive them less,
Yet fullest are they in themselves of light;
Such beams they yield as know no means to die,
Such heat they cast as lifts the spirit high.

Thomas Campion

from THE RIME
OF THE ANCIENT MARINER

For when it dawn'd—they dropp'd their arms,
And cluster'd round the mast;
Sweet sounds rose slowly through their mouths,
And from their bodies pass'd.

Around, around, flew each sweet sound,
Then darted to the Sun;
Slowly the sounds came back again,
Now mix'd, now one by one.

Sometimes a-dropping from the sky
I heard the skylark sing;
Sometimes all little birds that are,
How they seem'd to fill the sea and air
With their sweet jargoning!

And now 'twas like all instruments,
Now like a lonely flute;
And now it is an angel's song,
That makes the Heavens be mute.

Samuel Taylor Coleridge

from TO MUSIQUE,
TO BECALME HIS FEVER

Charm me asleep, and melt me so
 With thy Delicious Numbers;
That being ravisht, hence I goe
 Away in easie slumbers.
  Ease my sick head,
  And make my bed,
Thou Power that canst sever
  From me this ill:
  And quickly still:
  Though thou not kill
   My Fever.

Robert Herrick

ORPHEUS

Orpheus with his lute made trees
    And the mountain tops that freeze
    Bow themselves when he did sing:
To his music plants and flowers
Ever sprung; as sun and showers
    There had made a lasting spring.

Every thing that heard him play,
Even the billows of the sea,
    Hung their heads and then lay by.
In sweet music is such art,
    Killing care and grief of heart
    Fall asleep, or hearing, die.

William Shakespeare or *John Fletcher*

MUSIC GOD

He does not hear the struck string,
The stretched voice, the blown brass,
The sudden start, the sweet run
Of notes are not for him, alas.

Then what the measure, what the pitch,
Whereof he is acknowledged lord?
What the laws for less than sound,
And whose the silence whence a chord?

He will not answer save with eyes
That feed on distance all the while;
With more of pleasure here than there,
But most at some remembered mile

Too far for count, or so we say
Who cannot number save with ears;
Who cannot stand with him and see
Triangles perfect after years:

From grove to grove the singing base,
Then on to where two rivers cry;
Or so we say of three clear tones
That in eternal quiet lie.

Mark Van Doren

138

CHURCH-MUSICK

Sweetest of sweets, I thank you: when displeasure
    Did through my bodie wound my minde,
You took me thence, and in your house of pleasure
    A daintie lodging me assign'd.

Now I in you without a bodie move,
    Rising and falling with your wings,
We both together sweetly live and love,
    Yet say sometimes, *'God help poore Kings.'*

Comfort, I'le die; for if you poste from me
    Sure I shall do so, and much more.
But if I travell in your companie
    You know the way to heaven's doore.

George Herbert

TO MUSICK

Musick, thou *Queen of Heaven,* Care-charming-spel,
    That strik'st a stilnesse into hell:
Thou that tam'st *Tygers,* and fierce storms (that rise)
    With thy soule-melting Lullabies:
Fall down, down, down, from those thy chiming spheres,
To charme our soules, as thou enchant'st our eares.

Robert Herrick

from CHRISTIAN ETHICS

All music, sauces, feasts, delights and pleasures,
Games, dancing, arts, consist in governed measures;
Much more do words and passions of the mind
In temperance their sacred beauty find.

Thomas Traherne

140

TO HIS FRIEND MASTER R. L.,
IN PRAISE OF MUSIC AND POETRY

If music and sweet poetry agree,
As they must needs, the sister and the brother,
Then must the love be great 'twixt thee and me,
Because thou lov's the one, and I the other.
Dowland to thee is dear, whose heavenly touch
Upon the lute doth ravish human sense;
Spenser, to me, whose deep conceit is such
As, passing all conceit, needs no defence.
Thou lov'st to hear the sweet melodious sound
That Phoebus' lute, the queen of music, makes;
And I in deep delight am chiefly drowned
Whenas himself to singing he betakes:
     One god is god of both, as poets feign;
     One knight loves both, and both in thee remain.

Richard Barnfield

from NEW CHITONS FOR OLD GODS

EUTERPE: A SYMMETRIC

Euterpe, you must think us common queer.
With so much hi-fi FM stuff to
         hear : here
Not a soul in fifty knows your chirpy
Name—you Muse of Music, you, Euterpe!

David McCord

A MUSICAL CRITIC
ANTICIPATES ETERNITY

If Someone, Something, somehow (as Man dreams)—
Some architectonic spirit-strength omniscient,—
Has wrought the clouded stars and all that seems
World, Universe, and Life (poor, blind, deficient)—
   If this be thus, and Music thrills the spheres,
   And I go thither when my feet have trod
   Past Death,—what chords might ecstasize my ears!
   What oratorios of Almighty God! . . .

Yet, seeing that all goes not too well on earth
In this harmonic venture known as Time,
I'm not too optimistic of the worth
Of problematic symphonies sublime:
   And, though I listened aureoled and meek
   To compositions by the Holy Trinity,
   Who knows but I may write (in my critique)—
   "The music was devoid of all divinity!"

Siegfried Sassoon

MUSICIANS WRESTLE EVERYWHERE

Musicians wrestle everywhere:
All day, among the crowded air,
   I hear the silver strife;
And—waking long before the dawn—
Such transport breaks upon the town
   I think it that "new life!"

It is not bird, it has no nest;
Nor band, in brass and scarlet dressed,
   Nor tambourine, nor man;
It is not hymn from pulpit read,—
The morning stars the treble led
   On time's first afternoon!

Some say it is the spheres at play!
Some say that bright majority
   Of vanished dames and men!
Some think it service in the place
Where we, with late, celestial face,
   Please God, shall ascertain!

Emily Dickinson

THE RELIC

A murmuring in empty shells
Recalls the ocean's undertone,
But not a wisp of music dwells
In this small skull of dulcet bone—
A thrush's skull, miraculous
Among dead leaves and threads of ice,
This delicate contrivance was
The sounding board of Paradise.

Beneath the tree lies music's skull,
The tree a skeleton of spring,
And both, perhaps, are beautiful
Though leaves and thrush no longer sing;
But, growing old, I have a reason
For wishing some divine delay
Could hold a song beyond its season
And hide the thrush's skull away.

Robert Hillyer

from SONNETS TO ORPHEUS

First Part

A tree ascending there, O pure transcension!
O Orpheus sings! O tall tree in the ear!
All noise suspended, yet in that suspension
what new beginning, beckoning, chain, appear!

Creatures of silence pressing through the clear
Disintricated wood from lair and nest:
and neither cunning, it grew manifest,
had made them breathe so quietly, nor fear,
but only hearing. Roar, cry, bell they found
within their hearts too small. And where before
less than a hut had harboured what came thronging,

a refuge tunneled out of dimmest longing
with lowly entrance through a quivering door,
you built them temples in their sense of sound.

Rainer Maria Rilke
Translated by J. B. Leishman

146

from MICROCOSMUS

The heavens first in tune I'll set,
And from their music soon beget
A charm of power to make light fire
Skip to his sphere and earth retire
To her parched den. The subtle air
I'll calm from mists and make it fair,
And water with her curl'd waves sweep
The bounded channels of the deep,
That order may succeed, and things
Grow perfect from their lasting springs.
More light, ye spheres, in concord sound,
And with your music fill this round!

Thomas Nabbes

AT A CONCERT OF MUSIC

Be still, while the music rises about us; the deep enchantment
Towers, like a forest of singing leaves and birds,
Built, for an instant, by the heart's troubled beating,
Beyond all power of words.

And while you are listening, silent, I escape you;
And I run by a secret path through that dark wood
To another time, long past, and another woman,
And another mood.

Then, too, the music's cold algebra of enchantment
Wrought all about us a bird-voice-haunted grove;
Then, too, I escaped, as now, to an earlier moment,
And a brighter love.

Alas! Can I never have peace in the shining instant?
The hard bright crystal of being, in time and space?
Must I always touch, in the moment, an earlier moment,
And an earlier face?

Absolve me. I would adore you, had I the secret,
With all this music's power, for yourself alone;
I would try to answer, in the world's chaotic symphony,
Your one clear tone;

But alas, alas, being everything you are nothing—
The history of all my life is in your face;
And all I can know is an earlier, more haunted moment,
And a happier place.

Conrad Aiken

148

GO TO THE SHINE THAT'S ON A TREE

Go to the shine that's on a tree
When dawn has laved with liquid light
With luminous light the nighted tree
And take that glory without fright.

Go to the song that's in a bird
When he has seen the glistening tree,
That glorious tree the bird has heard
Give praise for its felicity.

Then go to the earth and touch it keen,
Be tree and bird, be wide aware
Be wild aware of light unseen,
And unheard song along the air.

Richard Eberhart

150

from THE HABIT OF PERFECTION

Elected Silence, sing to me
And beat upon my whorlèd ear,
Pipe me to pastures still and be
The music that I care to hear. . . .

Gerard Manley Hopkins

from BURNT NORTON

Words move, music moves
Only in time; but that which is only living
Can only die. Words, after speech, reach
Into the silence. Only by the form, the pattern,
Can words or music reach
The stillness, as a Chinese jar still
Moves perpetually in its stillness.
Not the stillness of the violin, while the note lasts,
Not that only, but the co-existence,
Or say that the end precedes the beginning,
And the end and the beginning were always there
Before the beginning and after the end.

T. S. Eliot

151

from A SONG FOR
ST. CECILIA'S DAY, 1687

From harmony, from heavenly harmony,
            This universal frame began:
When nature underneath a heap
            Of jarring atoms lay,
        And could not heave her head,
The tuneful voice was heard from high,
            'Arise, ye more than dead!'
Then cold, and hot, and moist, and dry,
            In order to their stations leap,
        And Music's power obey.
From harmony, from heavenly harmony,
            This universal frame began:
        From harmony to harmony
Through all the compass of the notes it ran,
The diapason closing full in Man.

What passion cannot Music raise and quell?
            When Jubal struck the chorded shell,
        His listening brethren stood around,
            And, wondering, on their faces fell
        To worship that celestial sound:
Less than a God they thought there could not dwell
            Within the hollow of that shell,
        That spoke so sweetly, and so well.
What passion cannot Music raise and quell?

        The trumpet's loud clangour
            Excites us to arms,

With shrill notes of anger,
And mortal alarms.
The double double double beat
Of the thundering drum
Cries Hark! the foes come;
Charge, charge, 'tis too late to retreat!

The soft complaining flute,
In dying notes, discovers
The woes of hopeless lovers,
Whose dirge is whisper'd by the warbling lute.

Sharp violins proclaim
Their jealous pangs and desperation,
Fury, frantic indignation,
Depth of pains, and height of passion,
For the fair, disdainful dame.

. . . . .

GRAND CHORUS

As from the power of sacred lays
The spheres began to move,
And sung the great Creator's praise
To all the Blest above;
So when the last and dreadful hour
This crumbling pageant shall devour,
The trumpet shall be heard on high,
The dead shall live, the living die,
And Music shall untune the sky!

John Dryden

INDEX OF AUTHORS

155

INDEX OF TITLES

158

INDEX OF FIRST LINES

161